Let's Make a

written by Jay Dale

illustrated by Cherie Zamazing

Tim was in the shed, too.

3

"Can I make a little boat?" said Tim.

4

"Yes," said Grandpa Josh. "You can make a little boat with me. It will be fun!"

5

Grandpa Josh had
a big box of wood.

"Can we make the boat
from wood?" said Tim.

"Yes," said Grandpa Josh,
"or we can make it from paper."

7

"No," said Tim.
"Let's make the boat from wood."
Grandpa Josh and Tim had lots of fun.

8

It was fun to make
a little boat from wood.

"It can be a red boat
or a green boat,"
said Grandpa Josh.

"Let's make it a red boat," said Tim.

"I like this little boat we made," said Tim. "Can we go to the river or down to the pond with the boat?"

"Yes," said Grandpa Josh.
"Let's go to the river.
It will be fun."

13

It was fun at the river!

Grandpa Josh and Tim
sat the boat on the river.
It went up and down.

"I like this little red boat," said Tim.
"And I like you, too!"